a Book for the Bog

CONUNDRUMS
FOR THE
KHAZI

they'll drive you round
the u-bend

Managing Editor: Simon Melhuish
Series Editor: Nikole G Bamford
Research: Gavin Webster
Design and Illustrations: Gary Sherwood

Designed and compiled by
Mad Moose Press
for
Lagoon Books
PO Box 311, KT2 5QW, UK
PO Box 990676, Boston, MA 02199, USA

ISBN: 1-904139-34-5

www.madmoosepress.com

www.lagoongames.com

Printed in China

a Book for the Bog

CONUNDRUMS FOR THE KHAZI

they'll drive you round the u-bend

1. You are on holiday on an island in the middle of a lake. The lake is in a remote part of Norway and there has never been a bridge connecting the island to the land (you were taken across in a rowing boat). Every day a tractor and wagon gives hay rides around the island to all the children. Puzzled as to how the tractor arrived onto the island, you ask around and find out that the tractor was not transported to the island by boat or by air. Nor was it built on the island. How might it have arrived there?

2. Mr and Mrs Brown have two daughters who each have a husband, two brothers and two sons. Can all the Browns fit into a four-seater car?

3. A farmer says: "I have ten or more daughters. I have fewer than ten daughters. I have at least one daughter." If only one of these statements is true, how many daughters has he?

4. There is a frog stuck in a 60-foot-deep well. How many days will it take the frog to get out if for every day he jumps five feet up, but then slides back three feet?

5. While walking across a bridge I saw a boat full of people. Yet on the boat there wasn't a single person. Why?

6. What falls but never breaks?

7. "I guarantee," said the salesman in the pet shop, "that this purple parrot will repeat every word it hears." A customer bought the bird, but found that despite talking to it all day, the parrot wouldn't speak a single word. Nevertheless, what the salesman said was true. How could this be?

8. You are participating in a race. Right at the end of the race you overtake the second person. In what position do you finish?

9. If there are two houses next door to each other and each has a garden and the man that lives in one of the houses has a peacock that lays an egg in the other man's garden, whose egg is it?

10. An egg salesman was asked how many eggs he had sold that day. He replied, "My first customer said, 'I'll buy half your eggs and half an egg more.' My second and third said the same thing. When I had filled all three orders, I sold out of eggs without having to break a single egg the whole day." How many eggs did he sell?

11. What happened in the middle of the 20th century that will not happen again for 4,000 years?

12. Who makes it, has no need of it. Who buys it, has no use for it. Who uses it can neither see nor feel it. What is it?

13. How many times can you subtract 5 from 25?

14. Sally bumped into her long lost uncle George who had gone to sea to seek his fortune before she was born. She had never met him, nor seen a picture of him, nor heard him described yet she recognized him immediately. How?

15. How many of each animal did Moses take on the ark?

16. In the garage behind your house, you have three big boxes. One of the boxes is labeled 'Apples', another one 'Oranges' and the last one 'Apples and Oranges'. The only thing you know is that none of the labels is correct. How can you correctly re-label all the boxes, if you are only allowed to take out one fruit from one of the boxes?

17. While on safari in the wild jungles of Africa, professor Anna Gram woke one morning and felt something in the pocket of her pajamas. It had a head and a tail, but no legs. When Anna got up she could feel it move inside her pocket. However, Anna showed little concern and went about her morning activities. Why wasn't she worried?

18. There is a barrel with no lid and some rum in it. "This barrel of rum is more than half full," said Charlie. "No, it's not," say Harry. "It's less than half full. "Without any measuring implements and without removing any rum from the barrel, how can they easily determine who is correct?

19. What can you give away and still keep?

20. In what year did Christmas and New Year's Day fall in the same year?

21. An Egyptian princess was born in the spring of 24 BC. If she died four months after her 62nd birthday, what year did she die in?

22. There are only two barbers in a small village. One of the barbers has a neatly trimmed head of hair. The other's hair is a complete mess. Which of the two barbers should you go to and why?

23. If an electric train is going east at 60 miles an hour and there is a strong westerly wind, which way does the smoke from the train drift.

24. Your mother's brother's only brother-in-law is asleep on your couch. Who is asleep on your couch?

25. Jim and Tom find a long piece of pipe on a building site. It's big enough so that each boy can just manage to squeeze into it and crawl from one end to the other. If Jim and Tom go into the pipe from opposite ends, is it possible for each boy to crawl the entire length of the pipe and come out the other end?

26. It's a mistake to hire amateurs, as the famous archeologist Doug Ittupp found to his great distress. One of his new staff came running in one day, all excited. He had just paid a local a great deal of money for an extremely valuable coin. As he said, "I've never seen one like this before, and I've been looking in museums for 30 years. It's a genuine Egyptian coin marked 100 BC — solid gold!" Then Doug sighed wearily and fired him. Why?

27. My first is in fish but not in snail
My second in rabbit but not in tail
My third in up but not in down
My fourth in tiara not in crown
My fifth in tree you plainly see
My whole a food for you and me.

28. Gladys Friday bought a used car for $500 and sold it to Mary Jones for $700. She later bought it back for $1000 and resold it for $1200. How much profit did Gladys make?

29. How is it possible to cut a square pie into eight equal pieces with only three cuts?

30. If a farmer has five haystacks in one field and four haystacks in another field, how many haystacks would he have if he combined them all in one big field?

31. There is a marvelous invention which makes it possible for people to see through brick walls. What is it?

32. The logic professor posted a notice on his class door: "Class is cancelled today on account of Spring. We will meet again at 1:00pm three days after two days before the day before tomorrow." What day does the class meet

33. Which two letters come next in this series: A E F H I K L M ? ?

34. You are working out some estimates for your boss. You can come up with a very good package for your nice little widgets, but the packaging may be too expensive. The cost of the widget and the packaging is $1.10, and the widget is $1.00 more than the package. How much will you have to tell your boss that the package for each widget will cost?

35. Can someone marry his brother's wife's mother-in-law?

36. What is the beginning of eternity, the end of time and space, the beginning of every end, and the end of every place?

37. Louis would rather have a rendezvous than a meeting. He prefers chocolate mousse to chocolate pudding. And he likes pasta, but not noodles. Which would Louis like better — a kimono or a bathrobe?

38. A farmer had 23 sheep. All but 9 died. How many did he have left?

39. What is it that is deaf, dumb and blind and always tells the truth?

40. What time is it when a clock strikes 13 times?

41. You are next to a river and have a five-gallon container and a three-gallon container. You need to measure out one gallon of water. How do you do it?

42. What is it the more you take, the more you leave behind?

43. A woman has seven children, half of whom are boys. How can this be possible?

44. A clock strikes 'six' in five seconds. How long does it take to strike '12'?

45. Said a certain young lady named Gwen
Of her tally of smitten young men
"One less and three more
Divided by four
Together give one more than ten"
How many boyfriends had she?

46. What is the significance of the following in the UK: thirty-four minutes past noon on 5 June, 1978.

47. You are driving a bus. Four people get on, three people get off, then eight people get on and 10 people get off, then six people get on and two more people get off. What color are the bus driver's eyes?

48. If you count 29 houses on your right going all the way to school, and 29 houses on your left coming home, how many houses in all have you counted?

49. A lily pad in a pond doubles in size every day. If on the 60th day the pond is filled with the lily pad, on what day is the pond only half full?

50. If you took five chocolates from a box which contained 21 chocolates, how many chocolates would you have?

51. A light bulb is hanging in a room. Outside the room there are three switches, of which only one is connected to the light. All switches are 'off' and the bulb is not lit. If you are only allowed to enter the room once to see if the bulb is lit or not (it isn't visible from outside), how can you determine which of the three switches turns on the light?

52. Tom and Tim were fishing in heavy seas when their trawler, The Right Angle, began to sink. They managed to send out an SOS before abandoning ship and help soon arrived. Tom was nearly saved and Tim nearly drowned. Which of them later donated a month's wages to the Lifeboat Institute.

53. Kenny had an after-school job at the Pet Food Emporium. His boss told him to stack 35 cartons of dog food so that each row of cartons would have one more than the row above it. How many rows of cartons did Kenny have when he was finished?

54. A farmer died, leaving in his will 17 fine horses to his three children, Ann, Bob, and Charlie. To Ann he left half his horses, to Bob a third of them, and to Charlie a ninth of them. How on Earth did they share out the horses?

55. Miss White, Miss Black and Miss Gray are out for a stroll together. One is dressed in white, one in black, and one in gray. "Isn't it odd," says Miss Gray, "that our dresses match our last names, but not one of us is wearing a dress that matches her own name?"
"So what?" said the lady in black.
Give the color of each lady's dress.

56. A circus strongman was boasting about his strength and went on about it for some time. An old gardener overheard and made him an offer, "Tell you what. I'll bet you $25 I can wheel a load in this wheelbarrow over there to the other side of the street that you can't wheel back."

"You're on," said the strong man. How did the old gardener win his bet?

57. Cindy is standing behind Ian and at the same time Ian is standing behind Cindy. How?

58. A family photo contained: one grandfather, one grandmother, two fathers, two mothers, six children, four grandchildren, two brothers, two sisters, three sons, three daughters, one father-in-law, one mother-in-law, and one daughter-in-law. What is the fewest number of people in the photo?

59. There was a train going along the track and a car coming along the road at a right angle to the train. They were both going at exactly the same speed and would have crashed in the middle had they met. Why didn't they?

60. How can you build pig pens so that you can put nine pigs in four pens such that each pen has an odd number of pigs?

61. A famous Italian composer died shortly after his eighteenth birthday — at the age of 76! How on earth could that be? He was born in February 1792.

62. Farmer Brown had nine ears of corn in his barn. A squirrel went into the farmer's barn and walked out with three ears each day. It took the squirrel nine days to take all the corn from the farmer's barn. Why?

63. Becky and Michael were playing in the house and accidentally smashed a window. "Oh, Mother will be so angry when she finds out," said Becky. "I know what to do," said Michael. He went outside and found a large rock and put it in the middle of the room. When Mother came home from shopping the children told her that someone threw a rock from outside and smashed the window. Mother was very angry, not because the window was broken, but because the children had lied. How did Mother know the children were not telling the truth?

64. Mr Hornbeeper drove off on a straight road with his eyes fixed on the setting sun in front of him. After driving for a mile, Mr. Hornbeeper found himself one mile east of his starting point! How can this be?

65. A man brought a jeweler six chains that each had five links. He wanted the jeweler to join all six chains together to make one long, closed, circular chain. The jeweler said, "It'll cost you a dollar for every link I open and close. You want me to join six chains, so the job will cost you six dollars."
"No, no," replied the man, "the job can be done for less." Is he right, and if so, how could it be done?

66. An Oriental prince, a great lover of chess, is on his death-bed and worries about the fate of his immense fortune. To which of his three sons should it go? His fortune is in the form of a chess set made of diamonds and rubies. He decides that his fortune will go to the son who plays exactly half as many games of chess as the prince has days left to live. The oldest son refuses, saying he does not know how long his father will live. The second son refuses for the same reason. The youngest son accepts. How does he respect his father's desires?

67. When James was nine years old he hammered a nail into a tree to mark his height. Ten years later, James returned to see how much higher the nail was. If the tree grew by four inches each year, how much higher would the nail be?

68. The expression, "Six of one, half a dozen of another" is commonly used to indicate that two alternatives are essentially equivalent, because six and a half dozen are equal quantities.
But are 'six dozen dozen dozen' and 'a half dozen dozen dozen' equal?

69. When this book first came out it was read only by a handful of very rich people. Now almost everyone has a copy and reads it frequently. But you cannot buy it in a bookshop or borrow it from a library. What is it?

70. A boat has a ladder that has six rungs. Each rung is one foot apart. The bottom rung is one foot from the water. The tide rises at 12 inches every 15 minutes. High tide peaks in one hour. When the tide is at its highest, how many rungs are underwater?

71. What are the two possible responses that correctly fill the blank in the following sentence? "This sentence has --- letters."

72. How much will a 38° angle measure when observed under a microscope that magnifies ten times?

73. You have six glasses in a row. The first three are full of juice, the second three are empty. By moving only one glass, can you arrange them so that empty and full glasses alternate?

74. Ten people, all wearing hats, were walking along a street when a sudden wind blew their hats off. A helpful boy retrieved them and, without asking which hat belonged to which person, handed each person a hat. What is the probability that exactly nine of the people received their own hats?

75. A woman with no driver's license goes the wrong way on a one-way street and turns left at a corner with a no left turn sign. A policeman sees her but does nothing. Why?

76. There are two lengths of rope. Each one will burn away in exactly one hour. They are not necessarily of the same length or width as each other. They are not of uniform width (they may be wider in the middle than at the end), thus burning half of the rope is not necessarily half-an-hour.
By burning the ropes, how do you measure exactly 45 minutes worth of time?

77. If you ripped the following pages out of a book, how many separate sheets of paper would you remove? The page numbers are 4, 5, 24, 47 and 48.

78. Rose is now as old as Joan was six years ago. Who is older?

79. What cannot be seen but only heard, and will not speak unless it is spoken to?

80. What determined the order of girls' and boys' names in the lists below?
Girls: Heather, Ellen, Laura, Anne, Nancy
Boys: Andy, Ted, Mike, Dick, Vic

81. Cressida didn't like to tell her age, so when she was asked, her mother answered for her. Her mother said, "I'm just seven times as old as she is now. In twenty years, she'll be just half the age that I will be then." How old is clever little Cressida?

82. When Maria went to get a passport, she had to give her date of birth, but under all circumstances she refused. When somebody asked how old she was, she said she was 21, mentally omitting all Sundays. Sundays she didn't work, so naturally she didn't get any older. How old was Maria really?

83. I got it in a forest but didn't want it. Once I had it, I couldn't see it. The more I searched for it, the less I liked it. I took it home in my hand because I could not find it. What was it?

84. In Tennessee, can a man marry his widow's sister?

85. Perhaps if you have ever been caught in the rain without an umbrella you will know the answer to this one. Joe Soaks found himself in a torrential downpour. Not only didn't he have an umbrella, he had no hat or any other object to place over his head. Nor was there any shelter around. Yet his hair didn't get the slightest bit wet. Can you explain why?

86. Nine thousand, nine hundred and nine dollars is written like this: $9,909. How fast can you work out the figures for this sum of money: twelve thousand, twelve hundred and twelve dollars?

87. Emily is taller than Ann and shorter than Dolores. Who is the tallest of the three?

88. If 70 percent of the population have defective eyesight, 75 percent are hard of hearing, 80 percent have sinus trouble and 85 percent suffer from allergies, what percentage (at a minimum) suffer from all four ailments?

89. There is a ferocious guard dog who follows your every move and is tied to a tree with a long chain. Your ball rolls away and ends up within the limits of the dog's chain. How can you safely get your ball back without harming the dog?

90. I have three friends. Two play football, two play tennis and two play golf. The one who does not play golf does not play tennis, and the one who does not play tennis does not play football. Which games does each friend play?

91. If you buy seven pounds of apples totaling 28 apples in all, how many apples can you put in an empty paper bag which will only carry 12 pounds without bursting?

92. Which is warmer, a two-inch thick blanket or two blankets one inch thick each?

93. Consider this sentence: Eleven plus two = twelve plus one. The question is, in what non-mathematical way does this equation also make sense?

94. What word, expression, or name is depicted below?
GIVE GET
GIVE GET
GIVE GET
GIVE GET

95. If the only sister of your mother's only brother has an only child, what would be your relationship to that child?

96. A trucker wants to drive under a bridge but finds that his rig is an inch higher than the bridge's clearance. The frustrated driver pulls to the side of the road and is checking maps to find his shortest alternative route when a small child comes up to him and says, "Hey, Mister, I'll tell you how to get your truck through." The suggestion worked. What was it?

97. A firewood merchant had a number of blocks to chop up for firewood. He chopped each block into 11 sticks. Assuming that he chopped at the average rate of 45 strokes per minute, how many blocks would he chop up in 22 minutes?

98. What was the biggest ocean in the world before Balboa discovered the Pacific Ocean?

99. I have a book where the foreword comes after the epilogue, the end is in the first half of the book, and the index comes before the introduction. What book is it?

100. Farmer Higgs owns three pink pigs, four brown pigs, and one black pig. How many of Higgs' pigs can say that they are the same color as another pig on Higgs' pig farm?

101. If six winkles and three cockles cost 15 cents, and you can buy nine cockles and three winkles for the same 15 cents, what will it cost to buy 100 cockles?

102. What occurs once in June and twice in August, but never occurs in October?

103. Who played for both Germany and Brazil in the 2002 World Cup final in Yokohama.

104. Robin Cluesoe is shipwrecked on a remote desert island. The only things he managed to salvage from the shipwreck are a piece of flint, a penknife, a ball-point pen, a can of lighter fuel and a packet of cigarettes. How can he make a cigarette lighter?

105. Two people were flipping coins. Each time, they bet one gold piece each on each game. At the end, one person had won three gold pieces overall and the other one had won three times. How many games did they play?

❧

106. When the two met, one was half the other's age plus seven years. Ten years later, when they married, the bride was thirty, but this time one was nine-tenths the age of the other. How old was the groom?

❧

107. There are 12 eggs in a dozen. There are 13 rolls in a baker's dozen. How many one-and-a-half penny stamps are there in a dozen?

❧

108. A boy and a girl are talking.
"I'm a boy," says the one with black hair.
"I'm a girl," says the one with red hair.
If at least one of them is lying, which is which?

❧

109. A clock on the wall falls to the floor and the face breaks into three pieces. The digits on each piece of the clock add up to the same total. What are the digits on each piece?

110. A farmer has 20 sheep, 10 pigs, and 10 cows. If we call the pigs cows, how many cows will he have?

❦

111. A sharpshooter hung up his hat and put on a blindfold. He then walked 100 yards, turned around, and shot a bullet through his hat. The blindfold was a perfectly good one, completely blocking the man's vision. How did he manage this feat? It wasn't luck.

❦

112. How far do you have to count before using the letter 'A' in spelling a number?

❦

113. Mother made 24 sandwiches for a picnic. All but seven were eaten. How many were left?

❦

114. A shopkeeper was experimenting with his scales one day and found several things. A jug weighs the same as a bottle. The same jug also balances out a mug and a plate. Three of those plates exactly equal the weight of two bottles. Based on those measurements, the shopkeeper knew exactly how many mugs it would take to balance a jug. How many?

115. In a singles tennis tournament, 111 players participated. They used a new ball for each match. When a player lost one match, he was eliminated from the tournament. How many balls did they need?

116. John and Jack's combined age is 91. John is now twice as old as Jack was when John was as old as Jack is now. How old are they?

117. Two men play five games of chess. They each win four games and there are no draws. How can this be?

118. If I dropped a ball into a bucket of water which is at 45° F, and also dropped another identical ball into an identical bucket of water at 30° F, dropping them at exactly the same time, which ball would hit the bottom of the bucket first?

119. You are walking through a field and you find something to eat. It doesn't have bones and it doesn't have meat. You pick it up and put it into your pocket. You take it home and put it on a shelf, but three days later it walks away. What is it?

120. Two sons are born to the same woman at the same time of the same day of the same year, yet they are not twins. How can this be?

121. Is it correct to say, "The yolk of the eggs are white" or "The yolk of the eggs is white?"

122. You have a silver pot and a golden pot. One of them contains a diamond, the other is empty. The silver has a label saying "This pot is empty." The golden pot has a label saying "Only one of these labels is true." If only one of the labels is true, where is the diamond?

123. What goes through the door but never enters or leaves the house?

124. A bookworm eats from the first page of an encyclopedia to the last page. The bookworm eats in a straight line. The encyclopedia consists of 10 1000-page volumes and is sitting on a bookshelf in the usual order. Not counting covers, title pages, etc, how many pages does the bookworm eat through?

125. Some freshman from Trinity Hall
Played hockey with a wonderful ball;
Two times its weight
Plus weight squared, minus eight,
Gave 'nothing' in ounces at all.
What was the weight of the ball?

126. Even though we may never have our own entry in the *Guinness Book of Records*, there is one record that each of us holds at some point in our lives. What is it?

127. Bobby Sox and Penny Laine are outside an ice cream shop. Penny tells Bobby, "I'll buy you an ice cream if you tell me the answer to this question: How is half of five, four?" Bobby thinks about this for a minute before answering and then Penny buys him an ice cream. What did Bobby say?

128. There is a tunnel with one railroad track going through it. One day two trains enter the tunnel on the same track going in opposite directions at exactly eight o'clock but they did not crash. How could this be?

129. I often go to the local police station, usually early in the morning or late at night when there aren't many people around, and destroy large numbers of fingerprints yet I am not a criminal. Who am I?

130. One day Kerry celebrated her birthday. Two days later her older twin brother, Terry, celebrated his birthday. Is this possible?

131. Three playing cards have been removed from an ordinary pack of cards and placed face down in a horizontal row. To the right of a King there are one or two Queens. To the left of a Queen there are one or two Queens. To the left of a Heart there are one or two Spades. To the right of a Spade there are one or two Spades. What are the three cards?

132. Pronounced as one letter,
And written with three,
Two letters there are,
And two only in me.
I'm double, I'm single,
I'm black, blue, and gray,
I'm read from both ends,
And the same either way.
What am I?

133. There are five sisters in the Smith family, and each one has one brother. How many kids are in the family in all?

134. Twice eight are ten of us, and ten but three.
Three of us are five. What can we be?
If this is not enough, I'll tell you more.
Twelve of us are six, and nine but four.

135. Alive without breath,
as cold as death,
never thirsty,
ever drinking,
when tired, never winking.
What is it?

136. At my favorite fruit stand, an orange costs 18
cents, a pineapple costs 27 cents, and a grape costs
15 cents. Using the same logic, can you tell how
much a mango costs?

137. A vintner recently passed away. In his will, he left 21 barrels (seven of which are filled with wine, seven of which are half full, and seven of which are empty) to his three sons. However, the wine and barrels must be split so that each son has the same number of full barrels, the same number of half-full barrels, and the same number of empty barrels. There are no measuring devices handy. How can the barrels and wine be evenly divided?

138. A man is condemned to death. He has to choose between three rooms. The first is full of raging fires, the second is full of assassins with loaded guns, and the third is full of lions that haven't eaten in three years. Which room is safest for him?

139. Ralph is a dashing young chap. Tall, dark and handsome, witty and charming, he is considered very attractive by most of the women he meets. To date, he's married 18 women yet none of the women have died, divorced him or committed bigamy. How?

140. On what day(s) of the year does the sun rise and set at the same time of day?

141. What would happen if you struck a match in a room filled with hydrogen gas?

142. If on a clock the hour hand moves half a degree every minute then how many degrees will the hour hand travel in one hour?

143. Imagine you are in a sinking rowboat surrounded by sharks. How would you survive?

144. A cowboy rode into town on Monday, stayed three days and nights and rode out on Monday. How can this be?

145. An old man wanted to leave all of his money to one of his three sons, but he didn't know which one he should give it to. He gave each of them a few coins and told them to buy something that would be able to fill their living room. The first man bought straw, but there was not enough to fill the room. The second bought some sticks, but they still did not fill the room. The third man bought two things that filled the room, so he obtained his father's fortune. What were the two things that the man bought?

146. If a man weighs 36kg plus half of his weight, how much does he weigh?

147. There are 20 people in an otherwise empty, square room. Each person has full sight of the entire room and everyone in it without turning his head or body, or moving in any way (other than their eyes). Where can you place an apple so that all but one person can see it?

148. With thieves I consort,
With the vilest, in short,
I'm quite at my ease in depravity;
Yet all divines use me,
And savants can't lose me,
For I am the center of gravity.
What am I?

149. I have many feathers to help me fly.
I have a body and head, but I'm not alive.
It is your strength which determines how far I go.
You can hold me in your hand, but I'm never thrown.
What am I?

150. What do you get if you multiply 8 by 2
twenty times?

151. Between noon and midnight, but not counting
these times, how often will the minute hand and
hour hand of a clock overlap?

152. My cousin Henry can always tell the score of a
soccer game before the game begins. How can that be?

153. The mother of Dave and Sue is going to have a baby. If it is a girl, Dave will have twice as many sisters as brothers. If it is a boy, Sue will have twice as many brothers as sisters.
How many children does their mother have now?

154. Bob and Carol and Ted and Alice all live in the same house. Bob and Carol go out to the cinema and when they return, Alice is lying dead on the floor in a puddle of water and glass. It is obvious that Ted killed her but Ted is not prosecuted or severely punished. Why?

155. Mary's husband's father-in-law is Mary's husband's brother's brother-in-law, and Mary's sister-in-law is Mary's brother's stepmother.
How did this happen?

156. On their way back to Pleasantville Lindsey, Allison and Monica took turns driving.
Lindsey drove 50 miles more than Allison. Allison drove twice as far as Monica. Monica only drove 10 miles. How many miles was the trip back to Pleasantville?

157. There is one in a minute and two in a moment, but only one in a million years. What are we talking about?

158. What arithmetic symbol can be placed between 2 and 3 to make a number greater than 2 but less than 3?

159. You enter a dark room. You have only one match. There is an oil lamp, a furnace, and a stove in the room. Which would you light first?

160. George, Helen, and Steve are drinking coffee. Bert, Karen, and Dave are drinking soda. Is Elizabeth drinking coffee or soda?

161. You have two hourglasses — a four-minute glass and a seven-minute glass. You want to measure exactly nine minutes. How do you do it?

162. Think of a four-letter common noun that names a tiny animal. Now change the second letter of the noun to the next letter in the alphabet. What larger animal, also four letters long, do you come up with?

163. Here is a question with a 'yes' or 'no' answer. It just happens to be phrased in a roundabout way, but that shouldn't disturb you if you can find a way to reduce it to its fundamentals.
"If the puzzle you solved before you solved the puzzle you solved after you solved the puzzle you solved before you solved this one, was harder than the puzzle you solved after you solved the puzzle you solved before you solve this one, was the puzzle you solved before you solved this one harder than this one?"

164. An emperor wanted to reward a servant for his hard work. He asked the servant what he wanted. The servant replied that all he wanted was some rice. The servant also said that he was very fond of playing chess and suggested that on the first square of the chess board be put two grains of rice, on the second two times two grains (four grains), on the third four times four (16 grains) and so on — each time multiplying the sum of grains on the previous square by itself. The emperor happily agreed, but he was soon to regret his decision, why?

165. You are inside a perfectly cubical room where each wall, the ceiling and the floor are mirrors. There is nothing else in the room. Assuming that you can still breathe, how many reflections can you see if you're facing one direction, and can look up, down, left and right?

166. What English word can have four of its five letters removed and still retain its original pronunciation?

167. What has four legs but only one foot?

168. Courtney is Allene's daughter's aunt's husband's daughter's sister. What is the relationship between Courtney and Allene?

❧

169. A cunning farmer, asked how many sheep he had, replied: "A third of my sheep are in the barn. A fifth are out to pasture. Three times the difference of those two numbers are newborn. And one is my daughter's pet. But there are less than twenty in all." How many sheep did the farmer have?

❧

170. A man was walking along some railroad tracks when he noticed that a train was coming. He ran towards the train as fast as he could and then stepped aside just as the train was about to hit him. Why?

❧

171. What will you find in the center of Paris that can't be found in London or Los Angeles?

❧

172. A woman gives a beggar 50 cents. The woman is the beggar's sister, but the beggar is not the woman's brother. How come?

173. Assign every letter of the alphabet its numerical value: A=1, B=2 and so on. Can you think of a seven-letter word for a vegetable whose letter values total only 21?

174. During a late party in London last weekend, I bet my friends during our midnight feast that the weather in exactly one week's time would not be sunny. How can I be positive I will win the bet?

175. One boy can eat 100 chocolates in half a minute, and another can eat half as many in twice the length of time. How many chocolates can both boys eat in 15 seconds?

176. A man bet his neighbor $100 that his dog could jump higher than his house. Thinking this not possible, the neighbor took the bet and lost. Why did he lose the bet?

177. An electrician and a plumber were waiting in line for admission to the International Home Show. One of them was the father of the other's son. How could this be possible?

178. When the fire alarm sounded in the 12-story building where he works, Stewart didn't hesitate for a moment. Instead of making for the stairs he jumped straight out of the nearest window. How did he survive?

179. He starts and ends two common English words. One painful in love, one painful in everyday life. Do you know what the two words must be?

180. Old coins are often worth considerably more than their face value, but why are 1999 cents worth almost twenty dollars?

181. There's a town in Ontario where 5 percent of all the people have unlisted phone numbers. If you selected 240 names at random from the town's phone directory, on average, how many of these people would have unlisted phone numbers?

182. My niece has trouble telling her left hand from her right, so I bought her a pair of reversible gloves, blue on one side and green on the other. I put a blue glove on her right hand telling her, "The blue hand is the right hand," and turned the other inside out so it was green. But when I went to put it on her left hand I noticed a problem. What is the problem?

183. I can be any color you can imagine. You see me everyday. Look around, you'll probably see some of me right now. What am I?

❧

184. The ages of a father and a son add up to 55. The father's age is the son's age reversed. How old are they?

❧

185. Two chicken breeders, Sonu and Monu were talking one day. In the course of their conversation they noticed a curious coincidence:
If Sonu sold seven chickens to Monu, then Sonu would have exactly as many chickens as Monu.
If Monu sold seven chickens to Sonu, then Sonu would have exactly twice as many chickens as Monu.
How many chickens do they each have?

❧

186. You are lost in a forest. The forest is between two villages. In village A live only liars — they always lie. In village B, people always tell the truth. You want to go to village B. Then you see a man from village A or B. You can ask him only one question.
Which question will you ask him to know for sure where village B is?

187. A prisoner is given two bowls, 100 red balls and 100 white balls. He is told to put the balls into the bowls any way he wishes, as long as there is at least one ball in each bowl. He cannot leave any balls out. A blindfolded judge will come in and reach into a random bowl and draw out a ball. If it is red, the prisoner dies. If it is white, he goes free. How should the prisoner arrange the 200 balls so that he has the greatest possibility of going free?

188. If it takes Polly the Painter one hour to paint a bedroom floor that is nine feet wide and 12 feet long, how long will it take her to paint the living room floor, which is twice as wide and twice as long?

189. What is the closest relation that your father's sister's sister-in-law could be to you?

190. A butcher goes to the market with $100 cash. He has to buy exactly 100 animals. There are cows, geese and chickens for sale. A cow costs $15, a goose is $1 and a chicken costs 25 cents. He has to buy at least one of each animal and he has to spend all of his money. What does the butcher buy?

191. If a redhouse is made from red bricks, a bluehouse is made out of blue bricks, a pinkhouse is made out of pink bricks, a blackhouse is made out of black bricks, what is a greenhouse made out of?

192. There are two plastic jugs filled with water. How could you put all of this water into a barrel, without using the jugs or any dividers, and still tell which water came from which jug?

193. A loving couple were traveling by bus in a mountainous area. The couple disembarked at a bus stop in a narrow gorge and the bus set off again. As the bus moved off there was an earthquake and a great rock fell on the bus from the peak of the mountain, crushing it. Everybody on board was killed. The woman turned to her husband and said, "I wish we had stayed on that bus." Why did she say that?

194. I keep one spare tire in my car. Last year, I drove 10,000 miles in my car, and rotated the tires at intervals so that, by the end of the year, each of the five tires had been used for the same number of miles. For how many miles was each tire used?

195. What breaks but never falls?

196. What has cities with no houses, rivers without water and deserts without sand?

197. Two cyclists are racing around a circular track. Pierre can ride once around the track in 6 minutes. Louis takes 4 minutes. How many minutes will it take for Louis to lap Pierre?

198. Three men rent a room in a hotel. The manager charges them $30 and gives them their key. After they have gone to their room he realizes that he has made a mistake. The price of their room should be $25 and he has overcharged them $5. He opens the till, takes out five $1 coins and calls the bellboy. He gives the bellboy the five $1 coins and tells him to give them to the new guests. En route to the room the bellboy realizes that it is going to be difficult to split five coins between three men so he decides to keep life simple and give them each $1, keeping $2 as a tip. The men have paid $9 each for their room, or $27 in total and the bellboy has $2. Where has the missing dollar gone?

199. A father is four times as old as his son. In twenty years, he'll be twice as old. How old are they now?

200. What is often brought to the table and cut and passed around, yet never eaten?

201. What can run but never walks, has a mouth but never talks, has a head but never weeps, has a bed but never sleeps?

202. Newspaper Headline:
"Workers Strike — Want to Make Less Money!"
What is going on?

❧

203. What can go up a chimney down, but can't go down a chimney up?

❧

204. Professor Mumbles held up a vial of bubbling liquid and said "Class, I have a substance in this bottle that will dissolve any solid it touches. I intend to..." A student from the back of the room interrupted the Professor and said, "No you don't!" How did the student know?

❧

205. I know what my job is, the point has been made.
You say I have a big head, and you're right, I'm afraid.
Put me in my place, and then leave me alone.
What I need most is someone to drive me home.
What am I?

❧

206. If you were walking down a country road and there was a sheep in front of two sheep, and a sheep behind two sheep and a sheep between two sheep, how many sheep would you see?

207. A farmer in California owns a beautiful pear treefrom which he supplies fruit to a nearby grocery store. The store owner has called the farmer to see how much fruit is available for him to purchase. The farmer know that the main trunk has 24 branches. Each branch has 12 boughs and each bough has 6 twigs. Since each twig bears one piece of fruit, how many plums will the farmer be able to sell?

208. How many gifts, in total, did I receive during the *Twelve Days of Christmas* according to the song?

209. Amir tied two sacks of salt to the back of his donkey and headed for the market to sell the salt. On the way they passed a stream and the donkey jumped in to cool himself. As a result a lot of the salt dissolved into the water, ruining Amir's prospects at the market but improving matters for the donkey because his load became much lighter. Amir tried to get to the market on the following days, but the donkey always jumped into the stream. Finally Amir decided to teach the donkey a lesson. He once again set out with the donkey and the two sacks.
What did Amir do differently this time so that after that day the donkey stopped taking a swim?

210. Five mice, Mindy, Marty, Muriel, Mabel and Mike, were nibbling the cheese on the kitchen table, but Whiskers the cat chased them back into their hole. Muriel Mouse made it back third and Mike Mouse was fourth. Mabel Mouse was after Mike and Marty Mouse was not second. Which mouse was first and which was last?

211. Vince sent his cousin a postcard from the lake where he was on holiday with his family. Instead of directly telling his cousin the size of the fish he caught, he wrote a puzzle:
The fish's head was 5 inches long. The fish's tail was the length of the head plus half the length of the fish's body. The body equaled the length of the head plus the length of the tail.
What was the total length of the fish?

212. Here are three series of letters. Each letter in each series is the first letter of a word. The words in each series are related. What are the next three letters in each series?
1. O, T, T, F, F, . . .
2. S, M, T, W, . . .
3. D, N, O, S, A, . . .

213. Find a familiar English three-letter word, using the following information:

RED has no common letter with it.

END has one common letter, but not in the correct place.

TIN has one common letter, in the correct place.

TIP has one common letter, not in the correct place.

AIR has one common letter, not in the correct place.

214. If you are standing on a hard floor, how can you drop an egg three feet without breaking the egg?

215. Imagine a world in which the colors of things have changed from what we consider normal. Assume the following changes:

Snow is now red.

Grass is now black.

The sky is now brown.

Blood is now white.

Soot is now green.

In such a world, what is the color of dirt?

216. If it takes 20 minutes to hard-boil one goose egg, how long will it take to hard-boil four goose eggs?

217. Tom is older than Sue, and Sue is younger than Mary, who is older than Tom. Who is the oldest of the three?

218. A group of flies are trapped in a sealed jar. You place the jar on a set of scales. The scales will register the greatest weight when the flies are:
1. sitting on the bottom of the jar
2. flying around inside the jar
3. neither, the weight is exactly the same in each case.

219. An ordinary American citizen with a clean police record but no passport managed to visit over thirty foreign countries. He was welcomed in each country, and left each one of his own accord. He did this in one day. How?

220. A truck leaving London for Edinburgh weighs exactly two tons (including the driver and everything in the truck). About halfway through the trip, it crosses a bridge that can only bear a weight of two tons — any more weight on it, and the bridge will instantly collapse. Just before the truck crosses the bridge, a two pound tree limb falls and lands on the roof of the truck and remains there as the truck crosses the bridge. But the bridge does not collapse. Why?

221. A woman was a window washer. One day, she slipped and fell off of a 40-foot ladder onto a hard concrete sidewalk. She did not get a scratch. How could this be?

222. Two hours ago, it was as many hours after one o'clock in the afternoon as it was before one o'clock in the morning. What time is it now?

223. Jake was standing on one side of a raging river, and his dog Scruffy was standing on the other side. "Come on Scruffy, come boy!" shouted Jake. Scruffy crossed the river, ran to Jake, and got a treat for being a good dog. The amazing thing was that Scruffy didn't even get wet! How did Scruffy do that?

224. The dog named Copper weighs more than Brandy but less than Pumpkin. Brandy weighs more than Jelly. Pumpkin weighs less than Jam. List the dogs in the order of their weights, starting with the heaviest.

225. These words all belong to the same logical family because they have something in common:
footloose
committed
successful
address
millennium
Which of the following words belong to the same family?
silly
ancestor
millstone
heedless

226. Sally, George and Frank were picking up their fast-food orders — a burger, a plate of fries and a slice of pizza. "Who ordered what?" asked the man at the counter. George said, "I didn't order the pizza." The boy who ordered the chips said, "Oh, I thought you did." That was all the man at the counter needed to know. Who got each order?

227. Suppose you have three balls and two paper bags. How can you put an odd number of balls into each bag?

228. Mr Black is a butcher, and head of the shopkeepers' club, which also includes a baker, a grocer and a candlestick maker. At their meetings, they all sit at a square table. Mr Black sits at the head of the table, on Ms Brown's left. Ms White sits on the grocer's right. Mr Pink, who faces Ms Brown, is not the baker. What kind of shop does Ms White have?

229. There are several chickens and rabbits in a cage with no other types of animals. There are 72 heads and 200 feet inside the cage. How many chickens are there and how many rabbits?

230. Bill is a keen chess player and often plays against his parents. He wins and loses against both parents, but his mother is a better player than his father. His parents offer to double his pocket money if he can win two games in a row out of three, with his parents alternating as opponents. Which parent should he play first to maximize his chances of winning two in a row?

231. If one blanket measures 6 square feet and another 6 feet square, which is the larger?

232. You are locked in a prison cell with a dirt floor, stone walls, no window but an open skylight very high up in the ceiling. There is nothing else in the cell except for a mattress and a metal cup and plate. How do you escape if the only way out is over the roof?

233. Mr Seibold has six daughters. Each daughter is four years older than her next younger sister. The oldest daughter is three times as old than her youngest sister. How old is each of the daughters?

234. This sentense contains two mistakes. What are the mistakes?

235. What is the largest number you can express in Roman numerals using one each and only one of each numeral?

236. What does man love more than life?
Fear more than death or mortal strife?
What do the poor have, what the rich require,
And what contented men desire?
What does the miser spend, the spendthrift save,
And all men carry to their graves?

237. Old MacDonald had a farm, and on that farm he had lots and lots of chickens. He knows that 20 chickens in three coups will hatch 30 eggs in 18 days. Can you work out how long it would take 30 chickens in 4 coups to hatch the same number of eggs?

238. A seagull has fallen into a hole in a rock in the cliffs that rise from a beach. The hole measures three inches in diameter and is three feet deep. Due to the depth of the hole, the seagull cannot be reached by hand. You cannot use sticks or canes because you could hurt the bird. How can you get the bird out?

239. Put a coin in a bottle and then stop the opening with a cork. How can you get the coin out of the bottle without pulling out the cork or breaking the bottle?

240. Eleanor found $4. Putting that $4 together with the money she had before her good luck, she now had five times the amount of money she would have had if she had lost $4. How much money did Eleanor have before she found the $4?

241. What is the one thing shared by all three items in the same group?

A
a cow
a shoe
a baby

B
a zipper
a shark
a comb

C
a potato
a hurricane
a person

242. A woman has three daughters who in turn, each have three daughters. If they all get together in one room...
a) How many pairs of sisters are present?
b) How many pairs of mothers and daughters are there?
c) How many pairs of aunts and nieces are there?
d) How many pairs of cousins are there?
e) How many pairs of grandmothers and granddaughters are there?
f) How many people are there in the room?

243. A boat can carry only 200 pounds. How can a man weighing 200 pounds and his two sons, each weighing 100 pounds, use the boat to cross a river?

244. There is one word in the English language that is always pronounced incorrectly. What is it?

245. Which is worth more, half a ton of silver dollars or a ton of silver half dollars?

246. The day before yesterday Cindy was 17. Next year she will be 20. How can this be?

247. Hanging over a pulley is a rope with a weight at one end. At the other end clings a monkey, of equal weight. What do you think will happen if the monkey begins climbing the rope?

248. Manuel's birthday is a month that has no a or e in its spelling. This year Manuel's birthday falls in the first week of that month and on a day of the week that has an e and a u in its spelling. When is Manuel's birthday this year?

249. In Okmulgee, Oklahoma, you cannot take a picture of a man with a wooden leg. Why not?

250. A clever thief in the olden days was charged with treason against the king and sentenced to death. The king decided to be a little lenient so he let the thief choose his own way to die. What way did the thief choose?

251. Bob is four years younger than Jo. But in five years' time Jo will be twice Bob's age now. How old are they now?

252. Kindly old Grandfather Lunn
Is twice as old as his son
Twenty-five years ago
Their age ratio
Strange enough was three to one
When does Grandfather celebrate his centenary?

253. Every day, a wife picks her husband up at the train station at 5:00 pm One day he arrives early, at 4:00 pm, and he decides to walk along the same road that his wife will be traveling. She meets him along his way, and takes him home from there. If he had waited at the train station, she would have arrived exactly at 5:00 pm. But having met him along the way, they were able to get home 20 minutes early. So what time was it when she actually picked him up?

254. You want to send a valuable object to a friend. You have a box which is more than large enough to contain the object. You have several padlocks with keys. The box has a locking ring which is more than large enough to have a padlock attached. But your friend does not have the key to any lock that you have. How do you do it? Note that you cannot send a key in an unlocked box, since it might be copied and your friend cannot send her own open padlock in case it accidentally locks in transit.

255. A carpenter was in a terrible hurry. He had to work as quickly as possible to cut a very heavy 10-foot plank into 10 equal sections. If it takes one minute per cut, how long will it take him to get the 10 equal pieces?

256. A man goes into a bar and asks for a whiskey. The barman asks, "Scotch or Irish?" "What's the difference?" the man inquires and is told that the Scotch costs 90 cents and the Irish costs $1. The man orders an Irish whiskey and places $1 on the counter. A moment later another man comes into the bar and says, "A whiskey, please," placing $1 on the counter. The man in the booth serves him an Irish whiskey. How did the barman know which whiskey the second man wanted?

257. How could you rearrange the letters in the words 'new door' to make one word? There is only one correct answer.

258. Two mothers and two daughters go to a pet shop and buy three cats. Each female gets her own cat. How is this possible?

259. What unusual property do the words FLOUR, TERN, and THIRSTY have in common?

260. A princess is told by her authoritarian father that the next day she will be married to one of two suitors. She will be allowed to make one statement the night before. If her statement is true, she will be married to the tedious Ernie Ennui; if her statement is false she will be married to the boorish Ivor Lottosay. What statement must she make to remain single?

261. Two strangers from different parts of America both build similar apartment buildings in their home towns. By chance, they both forget the same part of their project. They each, once again by chance, call the same national DIY shop and order the missing items. The prices they are quoted are as follows:

One will cost them $2.

Two will cost them $2.

Twelve will cost them $4.

One hundred and forty four will cost $6.

What was the item they needed?

262. A man walked home after having been out drinking. He walked down the middle of a deserted country road. There were no street lights to illuminate the road and there was no moonlight. He was dressed all in black. Suddenly a car that did not have its headlights on came racing down the road. At the last moment, the driver of the car saw the man and swerved to avoid him. How did he manage to see him?

263. There is a secret Christmas message in the following letters. Can you find it?

a, b, c, d, e, f, g, h, i, j, k, m, n, o, p, q, r, s, t, u, v, w, x, y, z.

264. The social club in Draperville had saved for the whole year to finance an outing to the big fair in Cornice County, about half an hour away. On a bright Sunday morning they set out in high spirits, looking forward to an enjoyable day at the fair. Ten minutes later, Mr and Mrs Sanderson, prominent members of the club, turned round and headed back towards Draperville. Yet 20 minutes later they, along with the other club members, arrived at their destination. They did not use any speedier transportation to catch up with their fellow members.
How did they do it?

265. How much dirt is in a hole six-and-a-half feet wide, eight feet deep, and five feet long?

266. The great Detective Shirley Locke-Holmes is hot on the trail of the perpetrator of some atrocious puns. 'Intent to deceive' is the charge, and she is now interrogating three suspects.
George says. "I'm innocent — Jane is too."
Jane says, "Sally did it, and George is innocent."
Sally says, "I'm innocent and Jane did it."
The guilty one lied, and the innocent both told the truth. Who is the perpetrator?

267. Dee Septor, the famous magician, claimed to be able to throw a Ping-Pong ball so that it would go a short distance, come to a complete stop, and then reverse itself. He also added that he would not bounce the ball off any object, or tie anything to it. How did he perform this trick?

268. Which three boys' names are anagrams of one another?

269. A bridge connecting two little towns is strictly guarded by a soldier who sits in a cabin right in the middle of the bridge. He has instructions to send back anyone attempting to cross the bridge. Roger lives in one of the towns and wants to cross the bridge to see his sweetheart. He stands at the foot of the bridge and studies the movements of the guard to see if there is any way he can cross over safely. He notices the guard stands sentry outside his hut for five minutes and then goes into his hut for another five minutes before he comes out again. Roger estimates if he runs very quickly he might just cross the center line in the five minutes the guard is in his hut, but then the guard would surely see him and throw him back. Could you help Roger get across?

270. Does your name influence your preferences?
CASE 1: Rhea prefers a comb to a brush. She reads stories about knights but not stories about ladies. She tolerates gnats, but she can't stand bees. If you want to please Rhea, should you give her a bouquet or a plant?
CASE 2: Robin dislikes pizza but loves ices, can't stand pie but enjoys cake, listens to music but refuses to dance, and reads magazines but not books. If you want to please Robin, should you give him a bike or skates?

271. In which sport do all the competitors except one move backwards toward the finish line?

272. How quickly can you find out what is so unusual about this paragraph? It looks so ordinary that you would think that nothing is wrong with it at all, and, in fact, nothing is. But it is unusual. Why? If you study it and think about it, you may find out, but I am not going to assist you in any way. You must do it without coaching. No doubt, if you work at it for long, it will dawn on you. Who knows? Go to work and try your skill. Par is about half an hour.

273. Several hundred years ago, a band of explorers were embarking on a sea journey to the far north which would last for three weeks. When they arrived, they planned on having a celebration meal of roast lamb. The problem they faced was keeping the meat fresh for three weeks. If they tied a rope to the meat and trailed it in the cold water, predatory fish would eat it. If they took ice and snow with them to keep the meat cool, the ice and snow would melt and the ship would fill with water. How could they keep the meat fresh until they arrived at their destination?

274. Ronald and Donald were at the swimming pool. "I can hold my breath for a whole minute," said Ronald. "Watch me." He dived into the pool and sure enough stayed under water for a whole minute. "That's nothing," said Donald. "I can stay under water for five minutes."
"That's impossible!" said Ronald. "No-one can do that!"
"Let's make a bet," said Donald. "I bet I can stay under water for five minutes."
Ronald agreed and Donald won the bet. How?

275. How far can a rabbit run into the woods?

276. What word is pronounced differently when the first letter is capitalized?

277. What can't you see that is always in front of you?

278. A barbecue grill holds two steaks at a time. It takes ten minutes to grill one side of a steak. What is the shortest amount of time it will take to grill three steaks on both sides?

SOLUTIONS

1. It was driven across when the lake froze in the winter.

2. Yes. The married daughters have both taken their husband's names.

3. If the farmer has any daughters there will always be two statements that are true. Therefore he has no daughters.

4. 29. The last jump was out of the well so he didn't fall back.

5. They were all married.

6. Night, rain or temperature.

7. The parrot was deaf.

8. Second.

9. Peacocks are males and can't lay eggs. A female is called a peahen and doesn't have the bright colors.

10. Seven eggs. Half of seven is three and a half, plus half an egg makes four eggs, leaving the salesman with three eggs. Half of three is one and a half, plus half an egg makes two eggs, leaving the salesman with one egg. If the final customer also buys half of all the eggs left (half an egg) plus half an egg they buy the remaining egg and the salesman is left with nothing.

11. A year that reads the same upside down (*1961* for example). The next one is *6009*.

12. A coffin.

13. Once. After that you are subtracting 5 from 20, from 15 etc.

14. He is her father's identical twin.

15. Moses didn't take animals on the ark. Noah did.

16. You pull a fruit out of the box labeled 'Apples and Oranges'. If you pull out an apple, attach the 'Apples' label to the box, if you pull out an orange attach the 'Oranges' label. Then, since you know that all the labels are wrong, you can simply switch the labels on the two remaining boxes.

17. She knew it was only a coin.

18. Tilt the barrel until the rum just touches the lip of the barrel. If the bottom is visible it is less than half full, if not, it is more than half full.

19. A cold.

20. They fall in the same year every year — New Year's Day just arrives very early in the year and Christmas arrives very late in the same year.

21 39 AD. There was no year 0. The system begins with the year 1 AD.

22. The one with the bad haircut. They cut each other's hair if there are no other barbers in town.

23. Electric trains don't give out smoke.

24. Your father.

25. Yes, first one boy crawls through, then the other.

26. The BC system didn't exist in 100 BC. It comes from the English for Before Christ and English didn't exist either in 100 BC.

27. Fruit.

28. $400.

29. Cut it into quarters with two cuts, then pile the pieces on top of each other and cut them all in half with one cut.

30. One. If he combines all of his haystacks, they all become one big stack.

31. The window.

32. The next day, or tomorrow.

33. N and T, the next two composed of entirely straight lines.

34. 5 cents.

35. No, it would be his mother.

36. The letter E.

37. Louis would like a kimono better than a bathrobe. He prefers things that have names borrowed from other languages.

38. 9.

39. A mirror.

40. Time to get the clock fixed.

41. Fill up the three-gallon container first. Pour it into the five-gallon container. Fill up the three-gallon container again and fill up the rest of the five-gallon container, and you should have one gallon left over in the three gallon container.

42. Footsteps.

43. All the children are boys, so half are boys and so are the other half.

44. 11 seconds. There is an interval of one second between each stroke. If the clock strikes six, there are five intervals. If the clock strikes 12 there are 11 intervals.

45. Gwen had 42 boyfriends.
42-1=41. 41+3=44. 44/4=11. 11-1=10.

46. The time and month/date/year are 12:34, 5/6/78.

47. You are the driver. What color are your eyes?

48. 29. You counted the same houses going and coming.

49. On the 59th day. It doubles every day, and if the pond is half full on the 59th day, then it is filled on the 60th day.

50. You took five chocolates so you have five.

51. Turn the first switch to 'on' and leave it like that for a few minutes. Turn it off and turn the second switch on. Now enter the room. If the light bulb is lit, then you know that the second switch is connected to it. If the bulb is not lit, then it has to be the first or third switch. Touching the light bulb will give you the answer: if the bulb is still hot, then the first switch was the correct one; if the bulb is cold, then it has to be the third switch.

52. Tim. Tim was nearly drowned but was actually saved whereas Tom was nearly saved but actually drowned.

53. Seven rows: eight cartons in the bottom row, two in the top.

54. 17 horses won't divide evenly so, to make it easier, they borrowed a horse, making 18 horses, which will divide. Ann got nine horses, Bob six, and Charlie two, making 17 in all. They could then return the borrowed horse.

55. Miss Gray's dress cannot match her name, so it must be white or black. Since the lady in black responded to Miss Gray's comment, Miss Gray must be wearing white. This leaves Miss Black wearing gray (since the only choices left for her are black and gray) and therefore Miss White is wearing black.

56. He put the strongman in the barrow.

57. They are standing with their backs to one another.

58. Eight — four children (two boys and two girls), their mother and father, and one set of grandparents.

59. The car went over a bridge.

60. Build three pens and put three pigs in each. Then build a fourth pen around the other three.

61. He was born on February 29; 1792 was a leap year. So he only had a birthday every fourth year. 1800 was not a leap year.

62. Two of the three ears were on the squirrel's head.

63. If the window had been broken from the outside, there would have been glass all over the floor.

64. Mr. Hornbeeper drove in reverse.

65. Yes, it can be done for $5. Open all the links on one chain and use them to join the others together.

66. He plays one game every two days.

67. It would be in the same place as trees grow from the top.

68. No. Six dozen dozen dozen is 6 x 12 x 12 x 12. A half dozen dozen dozen is just 6 x 12 x 12.

69. The telephone directory.

70. None. The boat rises with the tide.

71. The two possible answers are thirty-one and thirty-three. Thirty-one (because 22 letters in the original sentence plus 9 letters in thirty-one equals thirty-one); thirty-three (because 22 letters in the original sentence plus 11 letters in thirty-three equals thirty-three).

72. It will still be 38°.

73. Pour the juice from the 2nd glass into the 5th glass.

74. The probability is zero. If nine people have their own hats, then the tenth must too.

75. She is walking.

76. If you light both ends of one rope, it will burn away in exactly half an hour. Burn one rope from both ends and the other rope from only one end. Once the first rope (which is burning from both ends) finally burns out (and you know half an hour has elapsed), you also know that the other rope (which is burning from only one end) has exactly half an hour left to burn. Since you only want 45 minutes, light the second end of the rope. This remaining piece will burn in 15 minutes, totaling 45 minutes.

77. You would have four sheets of paper. The odd pages of a book are on the right side, and the even pages are on the left. Therefore, pages 47 and 48 are opposite sides of the same sheet of paper.

78. Joan is six years older than Rose.

79. An echo.

80. In the list of girls' names, the second letter of each name is the first letter of the next. In the list of boys' names, the second-to-last letter in each name is the last letter of the following name.

81. Four.

82. 24. She subtracted one seventh of her real age.

83. A splinter.

84. No, if he has a widow then he is dead.

85. He is completely bald.

86. $13,212

87. Dolores is the tallest, then Emily, then Ann.

88. 10 percent.

89. If the guard dog follows your every move you can shorten his chain by running round and round the tree, just out of his reach. He will follow you, winding his chain around the tree.

90. One plays none so the other two play all three.

91. One — after that the paper bag isn't empty anymore.

92. The two blankets are warmer because the air trapped between them acts as an extra layer of insulation.

93. 'eleven plus two' is an anagram of 'twelve plus one'

94. Forgive and forget.

95. It would be you.

96. Let some air out of the tires.

97. 99. He can make 990 cuts in 22 minutes (or 990 seconds). Each block needs just 10 chops to turn it into 11 pieces as the last chop makes two pieces.

98. The Pacific Ocean — even though it hadn't been discovered as such, it was still the biggest.

99. A dictionary. The word foreword comes after the word epilogue, the word end is in the first half of the dictionary and the word index comes before the word introduction.

100. None. Pigs can't talk.

101. $1. Cockles cost one cent and winkles cost two cents.

102. The letter U.

103. The band. They played the national anthems of the two teams.

104. By taking some of the tobacco out.

105. If one player won three games but finished losing three gold pieces, then that person must have lost six games so they played nine games in total.

106. The bride was 30, and the groom was 27.

107. 12. There are always 12 in a dozen.

108. The girl has black hair and the boy has red hair. If one is lying then the other must be lying too.

109. The sum of the digits on each piece is 26: piece 1: 11, 12, 1, 2 piece 2: 9, 10, 3, 4, piece 3: 5, 6, 7, 8

110. He still has 10. We can call pigs cows but it doesn't make them cows.

111. He hung his hat on the barrel of his gun.

112. You have to count to one thousand.

113. If all but seven were eaten, then there were seven left.

114. Three mugs.

115. There was only one winner. 110 players were eliminated in 110 matches so 110 balls were used.

116. John is 52 and Jack is 39.

117. They don't play against each other, but against different people.

118. The ball in the bucket of 45° F water hits the bottom of the bucket first. The 30° F water is frozen, and the ball stops when it hits the ice.

119. An egg.

120. They are triplets.

121. Neither, the yolk of the egg is yellow

122. The silver pot contains the diamond.

123. A keyhole.

124. On a book shelf, the first page of the first volume is on the inside so the bookworm only eats through the cover of the first volume, then eight times 1000 pages of Volumes 2-9, then through the cover to the last page of Vol 10. This means the worm eats through 8000 pages of text or 4000 physical pages.

125. Two ounces.

126. Everyone is the youngest person in the world at the moment they are born.

127. Remove F and E from 'FIVE' and you are left with IV, or four in Roman numerals.

128. One train entered the tunnel at 8:00 am and the other at 8:00 pm.

129 The cleaner.

130. Yes. At the time she went into labor, the mother was traveling on a round-the-world cruise. The older twin, Terry, was born first on 1 March. The ship then crossed the International Date Line and Kerry, the younger twin was born on 28 February. In a leap year the youngest twin celebrates her birthday two days before her older brother.

131. King of Spades, Queen of Spades and the Queen of Hearts.

132. An eye.

133. Six. The sisters all have the same brother.

134. The number of letters in each word, so twelve is six, nine is four etc.

135. A fish.

136. 15 cents. Each fruit costs 3 cents per letter.

137. Two half-full barrels are dumped into one of the empty barrels. Two more half-full barrels are dumped into another one of the empty barrels. This results in nine full barrels, three half-full barrels, and nine empty barrels. Each son gets three full barrels, one half-full barrel and three empty barrels.

138. The third. Lions that haven't eaten in three years are dead.

139. Ralph is a priest.

140. The sun never rises and sets at the same time of day. Except at the poles, the sun only rises in the morning and only sets in the evening. Even at the poles, it can't do both simultaneously.

141. Nothing. A match won't burn if there is no oxygen in the room.

142. 30 degrees.

143. Stop imagining.

144. His horse was called Monday.

145. A candle and a match. After lighting the candle, the light filled the room.

146. 72kg.

147. On someone's head

148. The letter V.

149. An arrow.

150. 16 twenty times. It doesn't make any difference how many times you do the sum — 8 x 2 is always 16.

151. 10 times.

152. Before the game begins the score is always 0-0.

153. Three boys and three girls.

154. Alice is a goldfish, Ted is a cat.

155. Mary's father married the sister of Mary's husband.

156. 100 miles (Lindsey drove 70 miles, Allison 20 miles and Monica 10 miles).

157. The letter M.

158. A decimal point.

159. The match.

160. Elizabeth is drinking coffee. The letter E appears twice in her name, as it does in the names of the others that are drinking coffee.

161. Start both hourglasses. When the four-minute glass runs out, turn it over (four minutes elapsed). When the seven-minute glass runs out, turn it over (seven minutes elapsed). When the four-minute glass runs out this time (eight minutes elapsed), the seven-minute glass has been running for one minute. Turn it over once again. When it stops, nine minutes have elapsed.

162. The first four-letter animal is 'gnat', and the next is 'goat'.

163. The one you did after the one you did before this one IS this one. In other words:
"...the puzzle you solved after you solved the puzzle you solved before you solved this one" is this one.
Hence the question may be rephrased this way: "If the puzzle you solved before this one was harder than THIS ONE, was the puzzle you solved before this one harder than THIS ONE?" So it's up to you whether the answer is 'yes' or 'no'.

164. On the fourth square the total is 256 grains, on the fifth 65,536, and on the sixth 4,294,967,296. We gave up trying to calculate what the sum would be on the last square!

165. None. There is no light source in the room, so there are no reflections.

166. Queue — it changes to Q.

167. A bed.

168. Courtney is Allene's niece.

169. 15 sheep.

170. The man was on a bridge over a river and had to run to the end of the bridge before he could get off the tracks. As he had nearly crossed the bridge, he continued in the same direction, running towards the train.

171. The letter R.

172. The beggar is a woman, the rich woman's sister.

173. Cabbage.

174. Because in exactly one week's time, it will be midnight again. The sun does not shine at midnight in London.

175. Both the boys eat 62.5 chocolates.

176. A house can't jump.

177. One is a man, the other is a woman. They are married and have a son together.

178. He jumped out of a ground-floor window.

179. Heartache and headache.

180. Because 1,999 cents comes to $19.99 or one cent short of $20.

181. None — the people with unlisted numbers don't appear in the phone book.

182. If you turn a glove inside out it fits the opposite hand so when I turned the left-hand glove inside out to make it green, it became a right-hand glove.

183. Paint.

184. The father is 41, the son 14.

185. Sonu has 49 chickens, Monu has 35.

186. Ask the man to point to the village he lives in. He will always point to village B.

187. He should put one white ball in one bowl and all the other balls in the other bowl. There is a one in two chance that the judge will pick the bowl with the white ball and the prisoner will go free. If he picks the other bowl, there is a 99 in 199 (the ratio of white balls to total balls) or nearly a one in two chance he will go free. Overall the chances that the prisoner will go free are approximately three in four.

188. Four hours. If the room is twice as long and twice as wide then the area is four times greater.

189. Your mother.

190. Three cows, 41 geese and 56 chickens.

191. Glass.

192. Freeze them first. Take them out of the jugs and put the ice in the barrel. You will be able to tell which water came from which jug.

193. If the couple had not alighted at the bus stop the bus would have continued on its way and passed out of the gorge before the earthquake caused the rock to fall.

194. Each tire has been used for four fifths of the journey. Four fifths of 10,000 miles is 8,000 miles.

195. Day, morning or news.

196. A map.

197. 12 minutes.

198. There is no missing dollar. The trick is in the phrasing of the question. In the end the men have paid $27 for their room — $25 to the hotel and $2 to the bellboy (unbeknownst to them). It is meaningless to add $27 to $2 as the problem suggests as you are adding what the men have paid to the tip (which came out of what they paid) and therefore are counting the $2 twice.

199. The father is 40 and his son is 10 years old.

200. A deck of cards.

201. A river.

202. They work at the mint and are tired of being overworked. They want to work less ('manufacture' less money).

203. An umbrella.

204. A substance that melts anything it comes into contact with would have melted the bottle.

205. A nail.

206. Three sheep walking in a file.

207. None. A pear tree produces pears not plums.

208. 364: for example, on the fifth day of Christmas, my true love gave to me five gold rings + four calling birds + three French hens + two turtle doves + a partridge in a pear tree.

209. Amir loaded the sacks not with salt but with sand. When the donkey jumped into the stream and got the sacks wet, they became much heavier.

210. Marty Mouse was first and Mabel Mouse was last.

211. The fish was 40 inches long: its head was 5 inches long; its tail was 15 inches; its body was 20 inches.

212. 1. S, S, E (for six, seven, eight)
2. T, F, S (for Thursday, Friday, Saturday)
3. J, J, M (for July, June, May)

213. Since the answer contains no E or D (as in RED), the only good letter in END is N.
Then the good letter in TIN is N, which is the third letter of the answer. I and R are not in the answer, so the good letter of AIR is A.
The A is not the first letter of the answer, so it must be the second. The good letter of TIP is P, which must begin the answer: PAN.

214. Hold it more than three feet above the floor.

215. Dirt is now blue. The puzzle consists of pairs that exchange colors. Since the sky is now brown, brown things become blue.

216. 20 minutes — four eggs can be boiled at the same time if the pan is large enough.

217. Mary.

218. Answer: 3. The weight depends on the mass of the jar (including flies) and the position of the flies does not change that. Their weight in flight is transmitted to the bottom of the jar by the air currents generated by their wings.

219. He is a postman delivering mail to foreign embassies, which belong to the countries who own the embassies, not the host nation.

220. The truck weighs exactly two tons when it set off. By the time it arrived at the bridge it had used more than two pounds worth of fuel so the tree branch made no difference.

221. She fell off the first rung of the ladder.

222. It's now nine o'clock in the evening.

223. There was a bridge over the river, and Scruffy crossed the bridge.

224. The heaviest dog is Jam, the next heaviest is Pumpkin, the next heaviest is Copper, the next heaviest is Brandy and the least heavy (or the lightest) is Jelly.

225. Heedless. (All the words in the family have two pairs of double letters.)

226. George got the burger, Frank got the fries and Sally got the pizza. We know George didn't get the pizza, so he could have got the fries or the burger. But someone else got the fries, so George had to get the burger. Furthermore, we know that it was Frank who got the fries, because he is the only boy in the group besides George. So that leaves Sally with the pizza.

227. Put one ball in each bag and keep the other ball in your hand.

228. You know that Brown is on the left side of the table, and Pink is on the right, since you are told that Black sits on Brown's left, and Pink sits opposite Brown. That leaves the bottom side of the table for White. Since White sits on the grocer's right, Brown is the grocer. If Pink is not the baker, White must be the baker. That means Pink must be the candlestick maker.

229. There are 44 chickens and 28 rabbits in the cage.

230. If he has to win two games in a row he must win the second game so it is to his advantage to play the second game against the weaker opponent. He must also win one game against the stronger opponent, and his chance is greater if he plays the stronger opponent twice. The first game should therefore be against his mother.

231. The one that measures six feet square. It is six feet on each side so its area is 36 square feet.

232. First, dig a hole in the dirt floor with the metal cup and plate. Second, pile the dirt from the hole up against the wall. Third, climb the pile of dirt and escape through the skylight to freedom.

233. From youngest to oldest, the six daughters are 10, 14, 18, 22, 26 and 30 years old.

234. First mistake: 'sentense' should be spelt 'sentence'. Second mistake: There is only one mistake in the sentence.

235. MDCLXVI (1,666)

236. Nothing.

237. 18 Days. The time an egg takes to hatch does not change with the number of chickens.

238. By gradually pouring sand into the hole. The bird will keep moving so that it is not buried in the sand, forcing it higher until it comes out.

239. Push the cork into the bottle, and shake the coin out.

240. Before Eleanor found the $4, she had $6. If she had lost $4 from the $6, she would have had only $2 left. The $4 she found plus the $6 she already had means she now has $10, which is five times the $2 she would have had if she had lost $4 instead of finding $4.

241. A. A tongue.
B. Teeth.
C. An eye.

242. a) 12.
b) 12.
c) 18.
d) 27.
e) 9.
f) 13.

243. First the two sons cross the river together. Then one son returns with the boat. The man then crosses the river. The son on the far side of the river now returns with the boat to pick up the other son and the two join their father on the far bank.

244. Incorrectly.

245. A ton of silver half dollars.

246. The statement was made on 1 January. Cindy's birthday is 31 December, so two days ago (the day before her birthday) she was 17, yesterday was her 18th birthday, she will be 19 this year (on 31 December) and next year (the year after this one) she'll be 20.

247. The monkey pulls down on the rope hard enough to pull itself up. This increases the tension in the rope just enough to cause the weight to rise at the same rate as the monkey.

248. This year Manuel's birthday falls on the first Tuesday in July.

249. You have to take a picture of a man with a camera, not with a wooden leg.

250. To die of old age.

251. Jo is 13, Bob is 9.

252. This year. He is 100, and his son is 50.

253. 4:50 pm since she saved 10 minutes in both directions.

254. Put the object in the box. Attach a lock to the ring. Send it to your friend. She attaches her own lock and sends it back. You remove your lock and send it back to her. She removes her lock.

255. Nine minutes. He only needs nine cuts to make 10 pieces.

256. The second man put $1 in change on the counter: a 50-cents piece, two 20-cents pieces and a 10-cents piece. If he had wanted Scotch whiskey, he would have put only a 50-cents piece and two 20-cents pieces on the counter.

257. 'one word'

258. There are only three women. They are the grandmother, mother and daughter of the same family so the mother is both a mother and a daughter.

259. Remove one letter from each and they each spell a number: FOUR, TEN and THIRTY.

260. "Tomorrow I am going to marry Ivor."

261. The people in the puzzle both forgot to add address numbers to their buildings. If each individual number cost them $2, then one (the number 1) will cost $2. The number one hundred and forty-four (1, 4, 4) is three digits, and so costs $6 .

262. He was returning home in the middle of the day, so anyone could have seen him.

263. No L (Noël).

264. The Sandersons were traveling by train, and decided to go to the dining car at the rear of the train for a snack.

265. None. There is no dirt in a hole.

266. Sally.

267. He threw it straight up in the air.

268. Arnold, Roland and Ronald.

269. Roger runs to the center point, then quickly turns and faces the direction he came from. The guard thinks he is coming from the other direction and forces him to go that way.

270. CASE 1: Give Rhea a bouquet. She likes words (such as her name) that have silent letters.
CASE 2: Give Robin a bike. He likes words (such as his name) that alternate consonants and vowels.

271. Rowing. The oarsmen face backwards and the cox of each boat faces forward.

272. It doesn't contain the letter 'e', the most common letter in the English language.

273. By taking a live lamb.

274. Donald held a glass of water over his head for five minutes.

275. Halfway. After that the rabbit is running out of the woods.

276. There are quite a few words that change pronounciation when they become place names, eg 'polish' as in buff or shine which becomes 'Polish' as in from Poland or nice and Nice or slough and Slough.

277. The future.

278. 30 minutes. First grill one side of two steaks for 10 minutes. Then flip over the first steak. Set aside the second steak for now, and grill one side of the third steak. Grill them for 10 minutes. Now the first steak is done. Put the second steak back on and grill the other side, and flip over the third steak. Grill for 10 more minutes. All three steaks will be grilled in 30 minutes.

mad moose press